Little S

written by Jay Dale

illustrated by Katy Jackson

"Mum," said Molly.
"Come and see Little Sam!"

"Little Sam," said Mum.
"Come to me!"

"No! No! No!"
said Little Sam.

Little Sam is in Molly's room.
"Mum," said Molly.
"Come and see Little Sam!"

"Little Sam," said Mum.
"Come to me!"

"No! No! No!"
said Little Sam.

Little Sam is in the kitchen.
"Mum," said Molly.
"Come and see Little Sam!"

“Little Sam,” said Mum.
“Come to me!”

“No! No! No!”
said Little Sam.

Little Sam is in the bathroom.
“Molly,” said Mum.
“Come and see Little Sam!”